RANGERS

THIS BOOK BELONGS TO:

____

(Sign or print your name here)

EASTERN NATIONAL • FORT WASHINGTON, PA

This book is dedicated to Chandler Dickenson, great-grandson of Russell E. Dickenson, eleventh director of the National Park Service. To the men and women who care for our national parks, Russ was a respected leader. He has passed on to Chandler his dedication to America's national parks and the task of caring for these special places. The future of our parks is in the hands of Chandler and young people like him. This book can help a new generation learn how park rangers care for America's national parks. Few careers are more rewarding or more important than that of a National Park Service ranger.

Eastern National provides quality educational products and services to the visitors to America's national parks and other public trusts. Please visit our online bookstore at www.eParks.com. To become a National Park Service WebRanger online, visit www.nps.gov/webrangers.

Designed and produced by Eastern National and Therese Cruse.

The National Park Service Arrowhead logo used with permission.
Allosaurus image from *Dinosaurs of Utah*, by Frank DeCourten. Illustration by Carel Brest van Kempen; reproduced by permission of the University of Utah Press.
'This land is your land' reprinted courtesy of Ludlow Music, Inc. Words and music by Woody Guthrie.
Other images courtesy of Independence National Historical Park and the National Park Service.

ISBN 1-59091-036-2. Printed in the United States of America.

WELCOME!

Hi! My name is Jason, and I live in a national park. It's really great! National parks are special places in our country. They protect things that are important to visitors from all over the world. Sometimes national parks protect beautiful mountains or lakes. Sometimes they preserve places where significant events happened, or where famous people lived.

My mom and dad are National Park Service rangers. Rangers do just about everything, from law enforcement and fire protection, to interpretation and scientific research.

When you turn the page you'll meet my parents and some of their ranger friends, and along the way you'll find lots of fun activities to do, like puzzles, mazes, coloring pages, stickers and more.

Ready? Let's go!

Ranger Donna

Natural Resource Protection

Resource rangers like my mom Donna protect natural things like forests and beaches, and plants and animals.

They learn about all the living things in their parks and make sure they go on living there for visitors to see and enjoy.

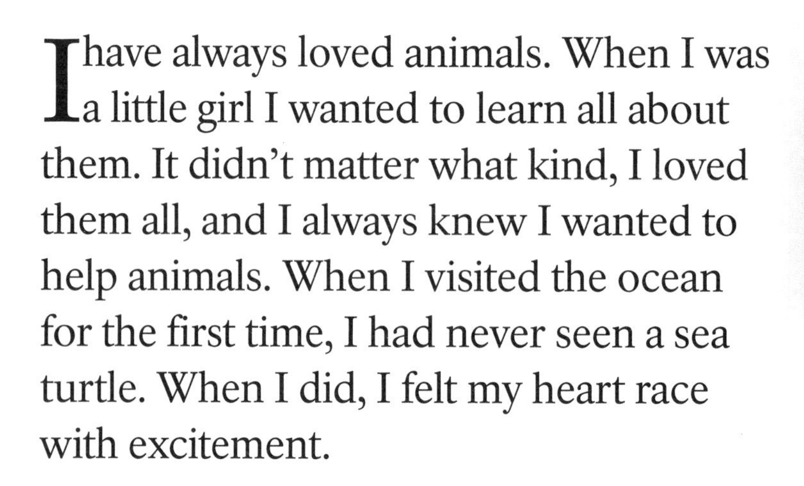

I have always loved animals. When I was a little girl I wanted to learn all about them. It didn't matter what kind, I loved them all, and I always knew I wanted to help animals. When I visited the ocean for the first time, I had never seen a sea turtle. When I did, I felt my heart race with excitement.

When I found out there were only a few sea turtles left in the world, I decided I wanted to help them. Most people thought sea turtles couldn't be saved from extinction. But I never stopped believing. Even though they are still endangered, there are many more sea turtles now than when I started.

I hope my son Jason and other kids will care about turtles and other animals as much as I do. What better job could a mom have than saving the world for kids?

COOL STUFF

...about natural resource protection!

Sticker FUN FACTS

Kemp's Ridley sea turtles are the most endangered of all sea turtles. Did you know that turtles return to lay their eggs at the same beach where they were hatched?

Find the Ridley Sea Turtle *sticker and place it here!*

Several of the plants and animals below are endangered. Can you guess which ones? Put an 'X' below the ones you think are endangered, then check your answers at the bottom of the page.

tiger salamander

spotted owl

ginseng

bay checkerspot

desert tortoise

black bear

beaver

giant garter snake

rainbow trout

ANSWER: The tiger salamander, spotted owl, ginseng, bay checkerspot, desert tortoise, and giant garter snake are endangered.

AN A-MAZE-ING ADVENTURE!

Sea turtles are endangered because of egg hunters with shovels, careless beach drivers, and hungry sea gulls and raccoons.

Help the baby turtle find its way to the ocean safely!

Ranger Steve

Fire Management

My dad is a fire ranger. Do you know that forests need fires to keep them healthy? Some pine cones open and release seeds only after being heated by a fire.

My dad goes all over the country working on fires. I miss him when he's gone, but I know he's doing an important job.

When I was a little boy, I thought firemen were the coolest. I also loved being outdoors. I wondered how I could do both when I grew up. Then I saw a park ranger on television putting out a fire and I knew what I had to do. I joined the National Park Service and learned all I could about fire.

My fire crew, both men and women, prepare forests for natural fires. Natural fires can be good for the forest. But sometimes a fire starts near a house or when it's hot and windy. That's not good, so we work hard to put those fires out.

Fires can be very dangerous. But I love being on the fire line keeping our forests healthy. What better job could a guy have?

COOL STUFF

...about forests!

Sticker FUN FACTS

Giant sequoia trees have fire-resistant bark. Did you know that sequoias can grow to over 300 feet high and weigh over one and a half million pounds?

Find the **Sequoia Tree** *sticker and place it here!*

SING-A-LONG

Here's a good campfire song. Ask your parents or grandparents if they know how the tune goes!

"This Land Is Your Land"

(CHORUS)

This land is your land, this land is my land,
From California, to the New York Island;
From the redwood forest to the Gulf Stream waters,
This land was made for you and me.

As I was walking that ribbon of highway,
I saw above me, that endless skyway;
I saw below me, that golden valley.
This land was made for you and me.
(CHORUS)

I've roamed and rambled and I've followed my footsteps,
To the sparkling sands of her diamond deserts.
And all around me a voice was sounding:
This land was made for you and me.
(CHORUS)

The sun came shining, and I was strolling.
And the wheat fields waving and the dust clouds rolling.
As the fog was lifting a voice come chanting:
This land was made for you and me.
(CHORUS)

Nobody living, can ever stop me,
As I go walking that freedom highway;
Nobody living can make me turn back,
This land was made for you and me.

FIRE TRUCK COLORING FUN!

Jason's dad Steve drives a truck like this when he goes on a fire. It's called a Type 6 engine and helps the ground crew get close to the fire.

Grab your crayons and color the scene below!

Ranger Maria

Backcountry Patrol

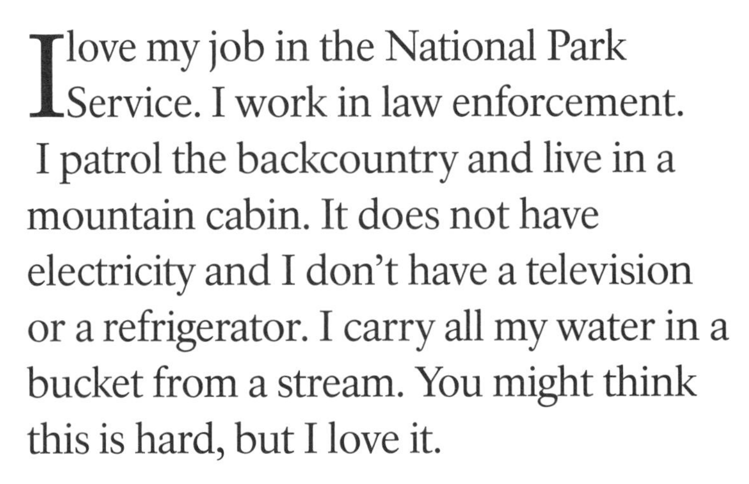

I love my job in the National Park Service. I work in law enforcement. I patrol the backcountry and live in a mountain cabin. It does not have electricity and I don't have a television or a refrigerator. I carry all my water in a bucket from a stream. You might think this is hard, but I love it.

Everyday my horse Ginger and I head into the wilderness. We make sure everything is okay. We look for lost hikers and move fallen trees off the trail. I help track bears for scientist rangers. I even put out campfires if people forget. That way campfires don't become big fires.

At night I sit by the stream and listen to owls hooting. I hear coyotes walking and bears sneezing. I hear Ginger eating her grain. I also hear silence, one of the sweetest sounds anywhere.

My mom's friend Ranger Maria works in the backcountry. Backcountry rangers are outside all the time. I think that's great, unless it's raining.

Backcountry rangers have to know how to use a map and compass to find their way, just like explorers!

COOL STUFF

...about the backcountry!

A compass can help you find your way in the wilderness. Did you know that a compass always points north?

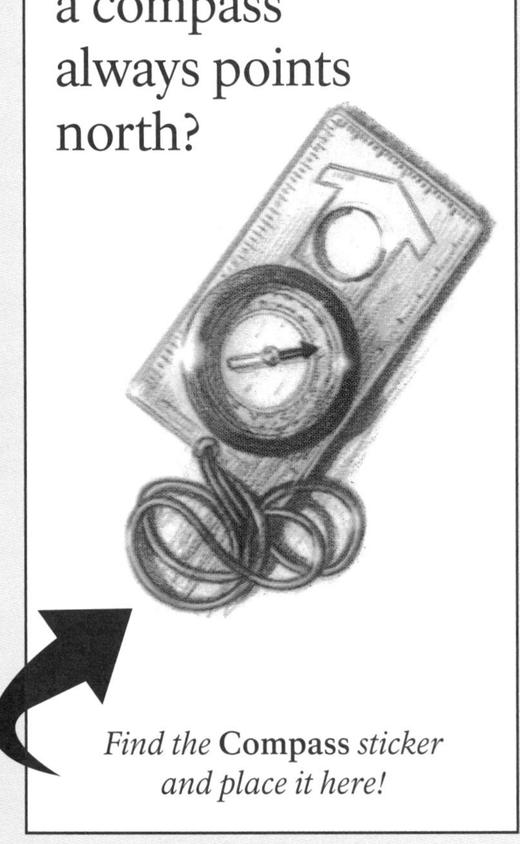

Find the **Compass** *sticker and place it here!*

These are some of the symbols you'll find when you visit a national park. Can you guess what they mean? Write your guess under each sign, and then check your answers below.

______

______

______

______

______

______

______

______

______

______

______

______

ANSWERS (from left to right): campfire, canoe access, bicycle trail, picnic area, fishing, lodging, gas station, hospital, hiking trail, horseback riding, swimming, food.

BACKCOUNTRY SEEK-N-FIND!

Can you find the 18 backcountry words hidden in the puzzle below? We found one of them for you. Check your answers in the back of this book.

Circle each word when you find it. The words are hidden up, down, sideways, backwards, and even diagonally!

```
K Z K W N A C O M I C L Z
Q G L Q V I H N X T O R O
Z V F X Y L A F Q S Y W L
C O M P A S S T T O O K A
T Q E L D D A S N O T T F
S R P O V I R T F U E H F
E R I F P M A C S K O S U
U H U R C N N X N E T M B
C C I Z A I O A W R R S V
S L X K B N L O E E X O D
E I O A E B G A M S A V F
R F C U N R M E W A T E R
I F B V N F V K R Y L V N
R A E B P Z J Y O R U K H
```

BEAR	CABIN	COMPASS	HIKER	MOUNTAIN	SADDLE
~~BLANKET~~	CAMPFIRE	COYOTE	LOST	RANGER	STREAM
BUFFALO	CLIFF	FOREST	MOON	RESCUE	WATER

Ranger Ken

Interpretation

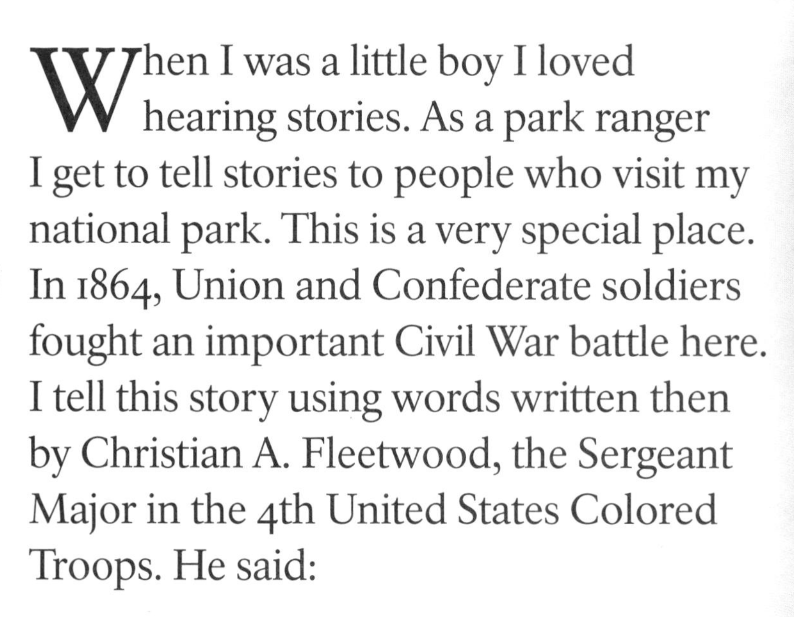

When I was a little boy I loved hearing stories. As a park ranger I get to tell stories to people who visit my national park. This is a very special place. In 1864, Union and Confederate soldiers fought an important Civil War battle here. I tell this story using words written then by Christian A. Fleetwood, the Sergeant Major in the 4th United States Colored Troops. He said:

> *"It was a deadly hailstorm of bullets sweeping men down as hail-stones sweep leaves from trees. They outnumbered us. It was sheer madness. I have never been able to see how I lived when so many others died."*

Because of soldiers like Fleetwood, both black and white, Union troops won the battle that day. For his gallant actions, Christian Fleetwood received the Medal of Honor. I'm proud to represent such an honorable and brave man and wear the uniform he wore.

My friend Ken is an interpretive park ranger in a Civil War park. 'Interpretive' means that he explains things in a way that visitors can understand.

Some interpreters tell stories about forests and animals. Some tell about American Indians, pioneers, or famous battles in American history.

COOL STUFF

...about interpretation!

Sticker FUN FACTS

Medals are awarded to people who do good things. Can you think of someone who deserves a medal?

Find the **Medal** *sticker and place it here, or give it to someone who deserves an award!*

The words below were used during Civil War times. Talk to someone using as many of these words as you can. See if others can guess what you're saying.

ARKANSAS TOOTHPICK (large knife)

BEEN THROUGH THE MILL (endured a lot)

BREAD BASKET (stomach)

FIT TO BE TIED (angry)

FRESH FISH (raw recruits)

GOOBERS (peanuts)

GRAB A ROOT (have dinner)

GREENBACKS (Union paper currency)

HUNKEY DOREY (okay or good)

JAILBIRD (criminal)

PLAYED OUT (worn out)

POSSUM (a buddy)

SAWBONES (surgeon)

SKEDADDLE (run, scatter, retreat)

SNUG-AS-A-BUG (comfortable or cozy)

TOEING THE MARK (obeying orders)

A MUSICAL CONNECTION!

Young boys often carried a musical instrument during the Civil War. Its sound led soldiers into battle .

Connect the dots to see one of the instruments they played!

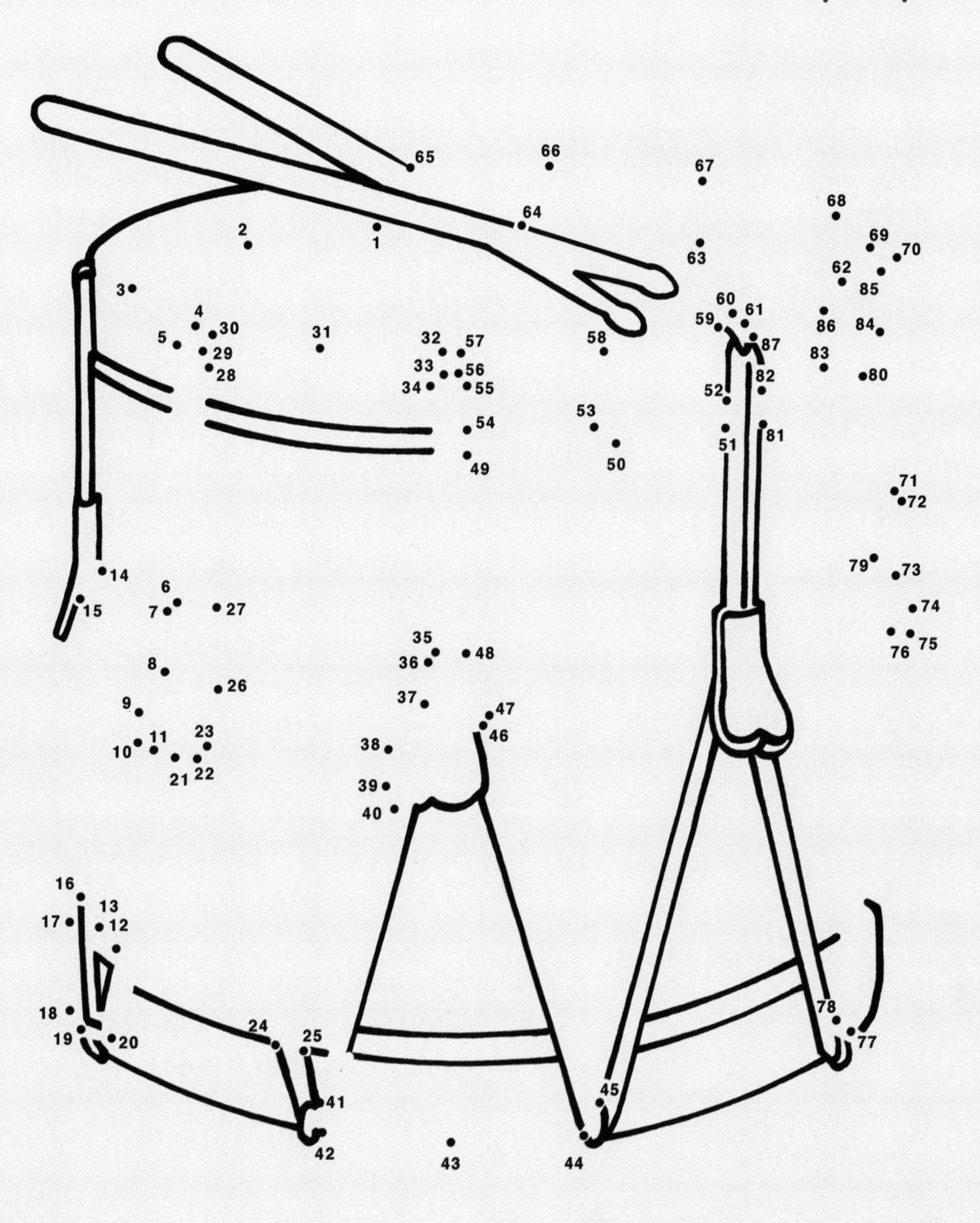

Ranger Dan

Scientist

We met Ranger Dan on our vacation to his park. Dan is a scientist. He studies things in the outdoors like plants and animals.

Scientists also study the lives of people who lived long ago. They even study bones and rocks! They learn as much as they can so that we can take better care of our parks.

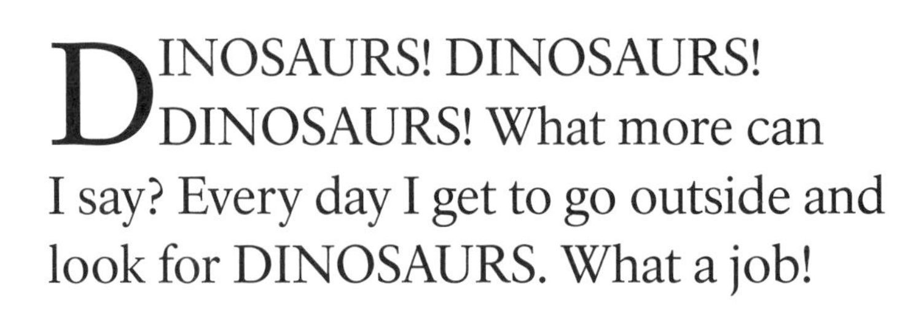

DINOSAURS! DINOSAURS! DINOSAURS! What more can I say? Every day I get to go outside and look for DINOSAURS. What a job!

One day as I was exploring in the park I saw a fossil poking from a hill. It was a dinosaur toe. I thought it was the only one. Then I discovered the whole foot! My dinosaur team and I came back the next day. We very carefully dug out the rest of the fossil bones. It took a whole year. When we were done we discovered it was a new kind of dinosaur. We were truly excited.

We love finding dinosaur skeletons, but they don't tell us everything about how the dinosaur lived. We study other fossils like leaves and pollen that tell us what the world was like back then.

I have an important job. I want to figure out why dinosaurs became extinct so we can save today's animals from the same end.

COOL STUFF

...about science!

Sticker FUN FACTS

Fossils are the remains of animals and plants preserved in rock. Did you know that very few plants and animals become fossils?

Find the **Dinosaur** *sticker and place it here!*

Below are some tools that Ranger Dan uses during the day. Match the tools on the left with the words on the right. We did the first one for you!

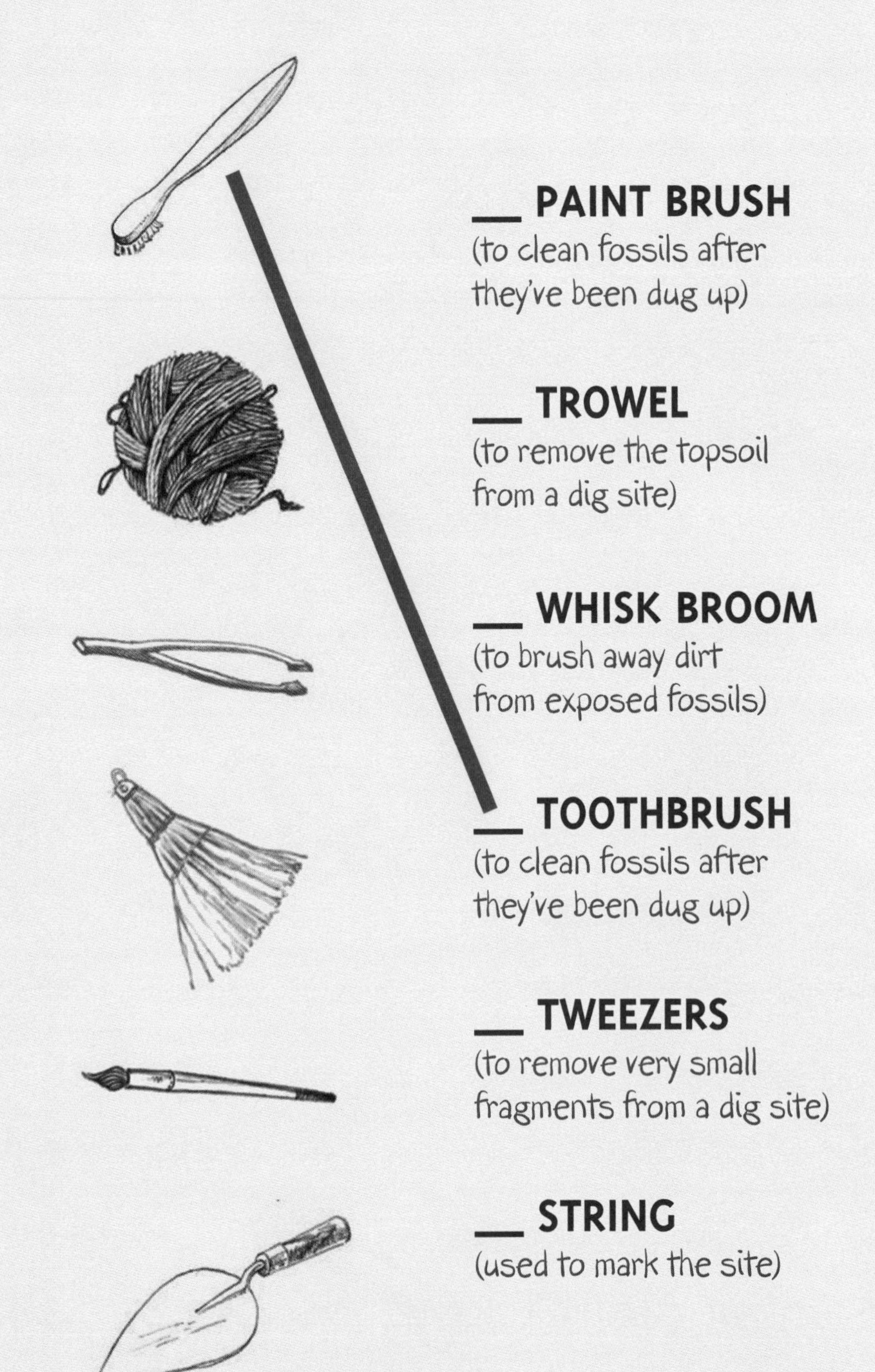

__ **PAINT BRUSH**
(to clean fossils after they've been dug up)

__ **TROWEL**
(to remove the topsoil from a dig site)

__ **WHISK BROOM**
(to brush away dirt from exposed fossils)

__ **TOOTHBRUSH**
(to clean fossils after they've been dug up)

__ **TWEEZERS**
(to remove very small fragments from a dig site)

__ **STRING**
(used to mark the site)

SOLVE THE DINO-PUZZLER!

The Allosaurus dinosaur that Dan found lived about 150 million years ago.

Find the jumbled stickers in the middle of the book and put them in the correct order below to see the Allosaurus!

Ranger Dakota

Search and Rescue

Sometimes my dad works with Ranger Dakota. She helps hikers who are hurt or lost, and she also patrols the trails and enforces laws.

She gives advice to people who aren't experienced hikers or boaters so they can stay safe and have fun!

Sometimes people get hurt or lost when they go hiking. Most of the time it's because they are not prepared. Maybe they aren't used to being outside in the heat. Or they don't carry enough water to drink. Sometimes they twist an ankle. Now and then people fall. Rescue rangers are ready for anything.

When I was a kid, my family visited national parks. We went for hikes. I really liked it. One day we met a ranger hiking the trails. I didn't know you could do that for a job! I thought, "Hey, I could do that when I grow up!" And here I am.

You might think that rescuing people is scary. Sometimes it is, but we are very careful and practice a lot. We take lessons from doctors so we will know what to do if someone is hurt. To me, saving people's lives is the most important job in the world.

COOL STUFF

...about hiking safety!

Sticker FUN FACTS

Rescue rangers carry first aid kits to help people who get hurt while hiking in national parks.

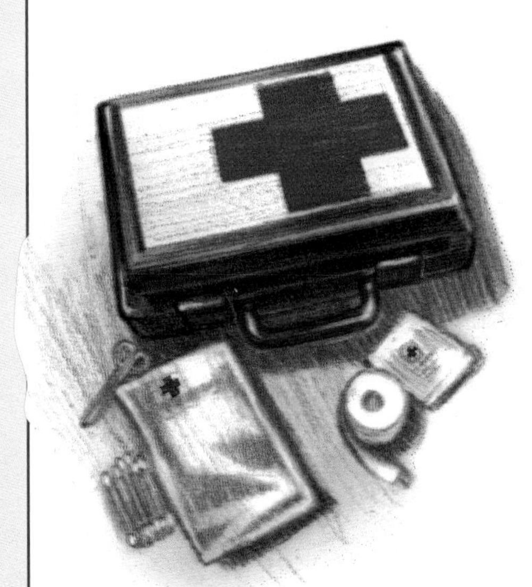

Find the **First Aid Kit** *sticker and place it here!*

My Hiking Journal...

Today is ______________________

I am hiking in ______________________

The distance I hiked is ______________________

The weather is ______________________

The best thing I did today was ______________________

____

The worst thing I did today was ______________________

____

Something new I learned today is ______________________

____

The most unusual thing I saw today was ______________________

____

Today I Feel: ❑ Happy ❑ Sad ❑ Helpful ❑ Tired ❑ Hungry ❑ Silly

Safe Hiking Checklist...

- ✓ Always carry water and snacks
- ✓ Always hike with a buddy
- ✓ Wear good hiking shoes and layers of clothing
- ✓ Stay on marked trails
- ✓ Tell an adult where you are going

BACKCOUNTRY BINGO!

You and a friend can play Backcountry Bingo.

Select a bingo card. Then, when one of you spots one of the items below, put an "X" on that square....

...and the first person to cross out four squares across, down, or diagonally, wins.

Good luck!

Ranger Kevin

Historian

My mom went to ranger school with Kevin. He knows a lot about people and events from the past.

Kevin helps preserve things important to our history, like Native American dwellings, battlefields, historic houses, artifacts (objects from the past), ideas, and sacred places.

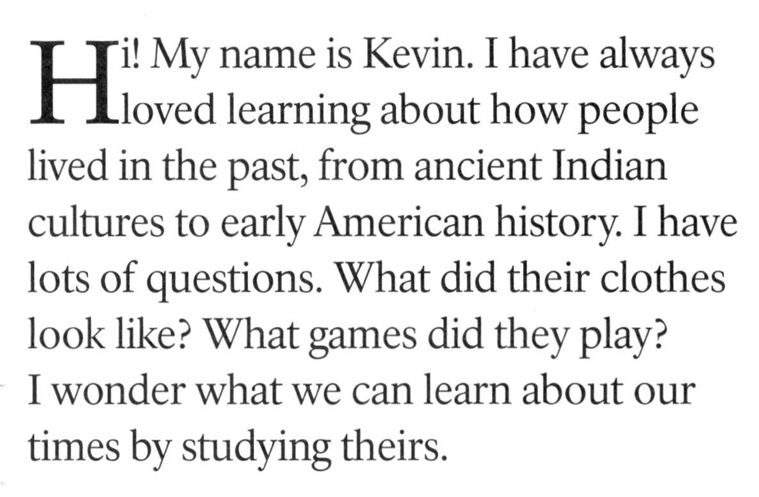

Hi! My name is Kevin. I have always loved learning about how people lived in the past, from ancient Indian cultures to early American history. I have lots of questions. What did their clothes look like? What games did they play? I wonder what we can learn about our times by studying theirs.

To learn about what happened in the past, I read letters people wrote long ago. I read diaries they kept and books they wrote. From these I learn what people did and thought about in their everyday lives. I can also see how their actions led to future events.

I work in a park where people did very important things. Two hundred years ago they wrote rules and laws we still live by today. I've learned how hard they struggled to decide what was best for our nation. It is important to save these stories so we will remember who we are as a people.

Fine

COOL STUFF

...about history!

Sticker FUN FACTS

Did you know that the Arrowhead is the official symbol of the National Park Service? Rangers wear the Arrowhead on their uniforms.

Find the **Arrowhead** *sticker and place it here!*

Why are they famous?

Do you recognize these famous Americans? Write down why you think they are famous next to each picture, then check your answers in the back of the book...

Name: **Martin Luther King, Jr.**

Why is he famous? ____________

____

____

____

Name: **Thomas Jefferson**

Why is he famous? ____________

____

____

____

Name: **Clara Barton**

Why is she famous? ____________

____

____

____

Name: **The Liberty Bell**

Why is it famous? ____________

____

____

____

TIME TUNNEL:
WHAT DOESN'T BELONG?

GOODBYE!

Didn't I tell you that national park rangers can do just about everything?
Together they protect our most special places.

Park rangers are my heroes. Because of them, national parks will be here for us when we grow up. Anyone who is curious and brave and loves history or the outdoors can be a park ranger.

How about you?